Countryside to colour

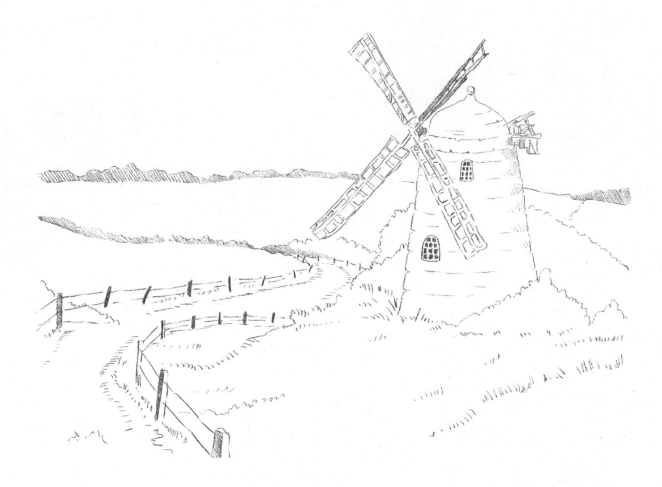

Published by: W.F. GRAHAM (NORTHAMPTON) LTD. NN3 6RT

www.wfgraham.co.uk   e-mail : books@wfgraham.co.uk

Illustrated by: **Katy Dynes**   e-mail : poppyk2@hotmail.com   Tel: 07966 167056

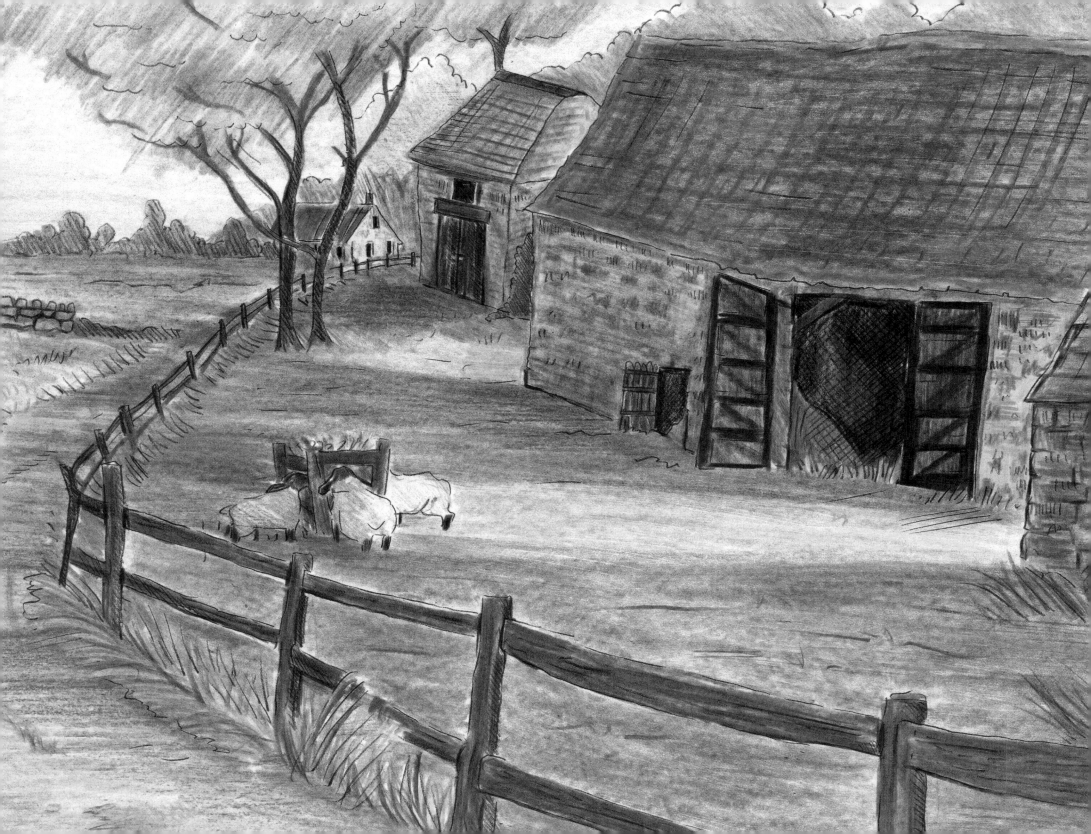

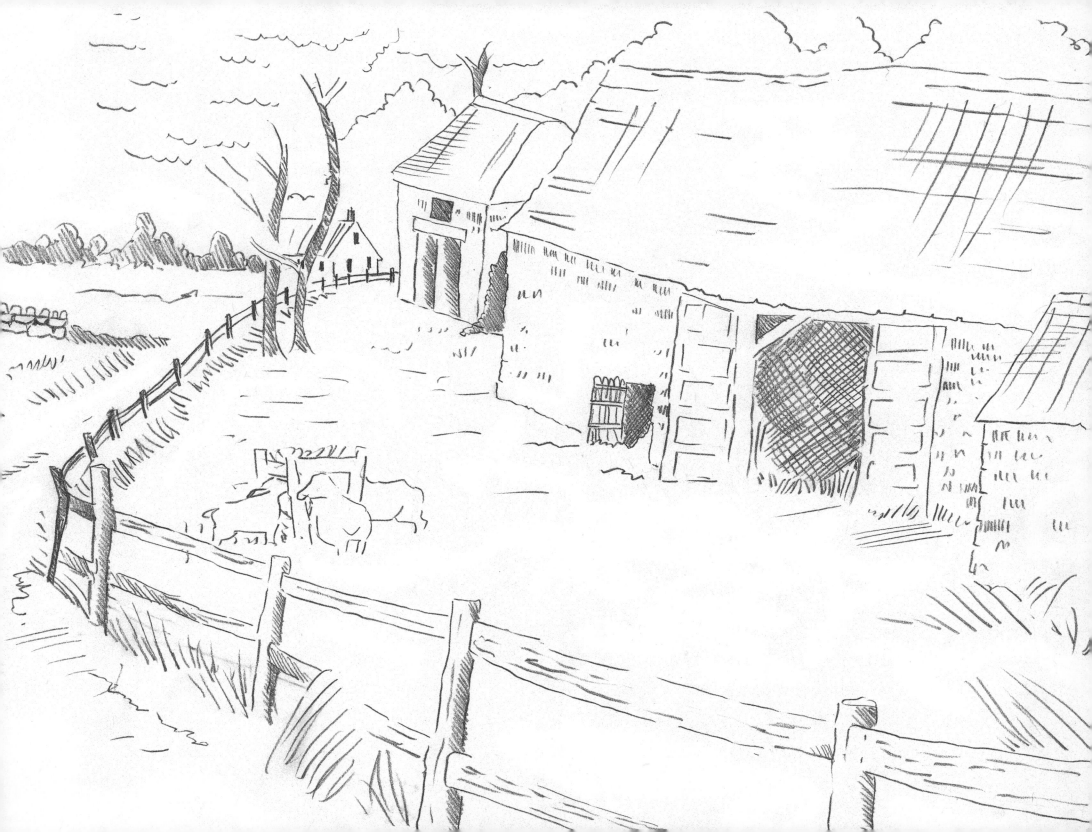

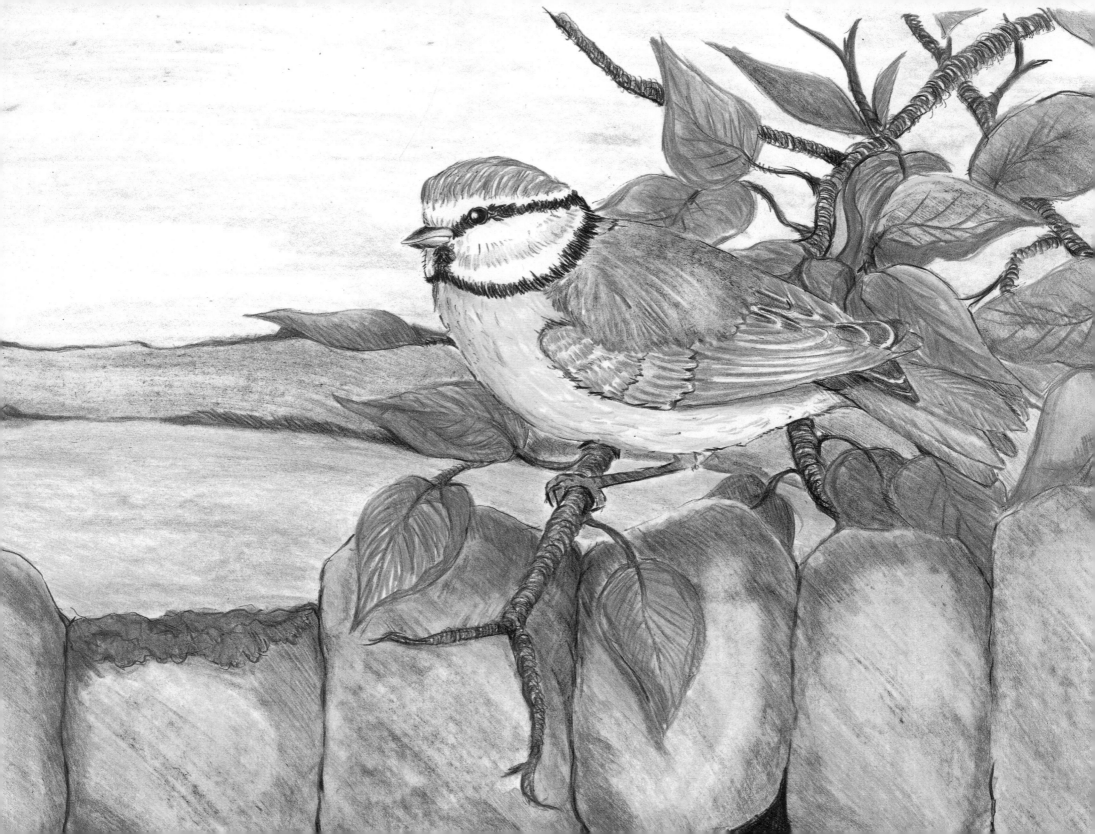

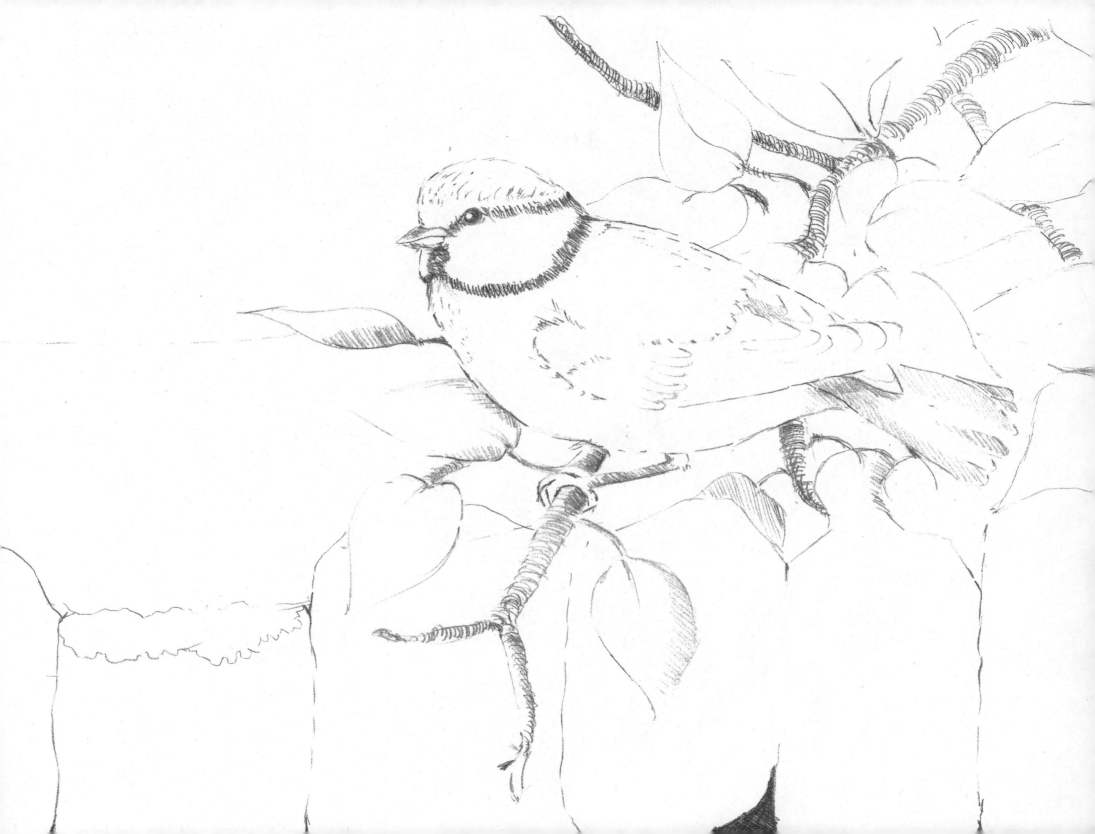

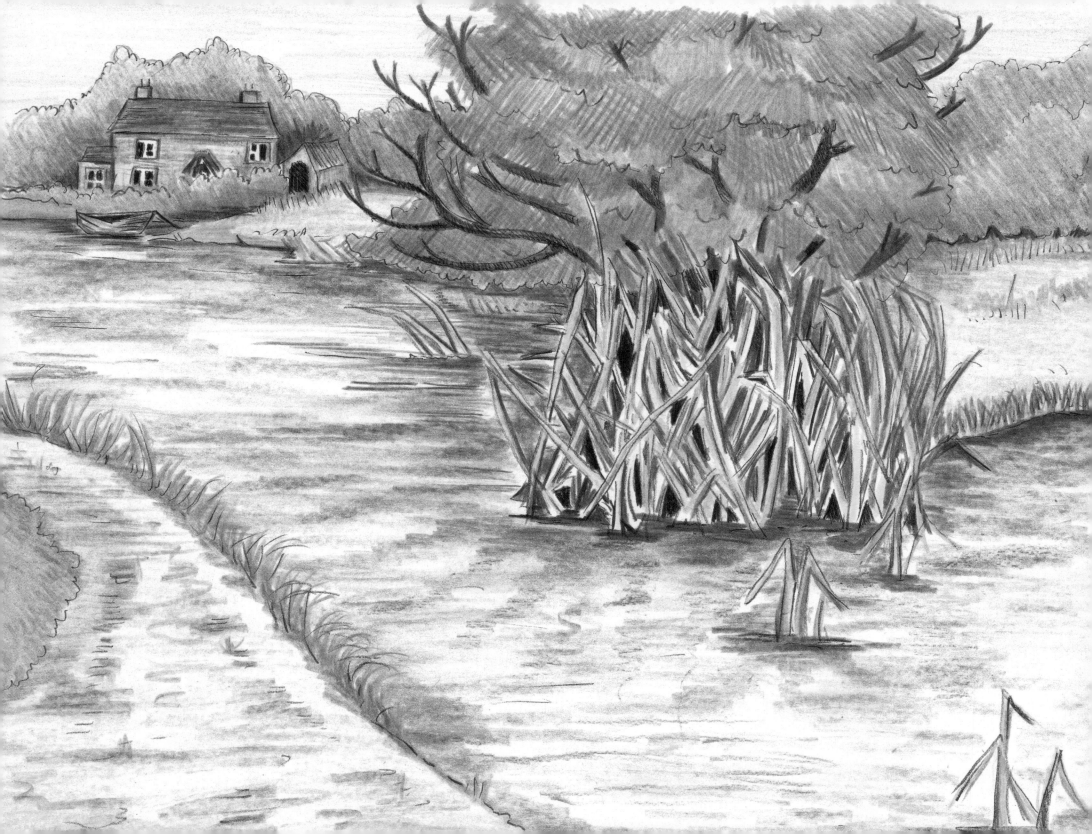

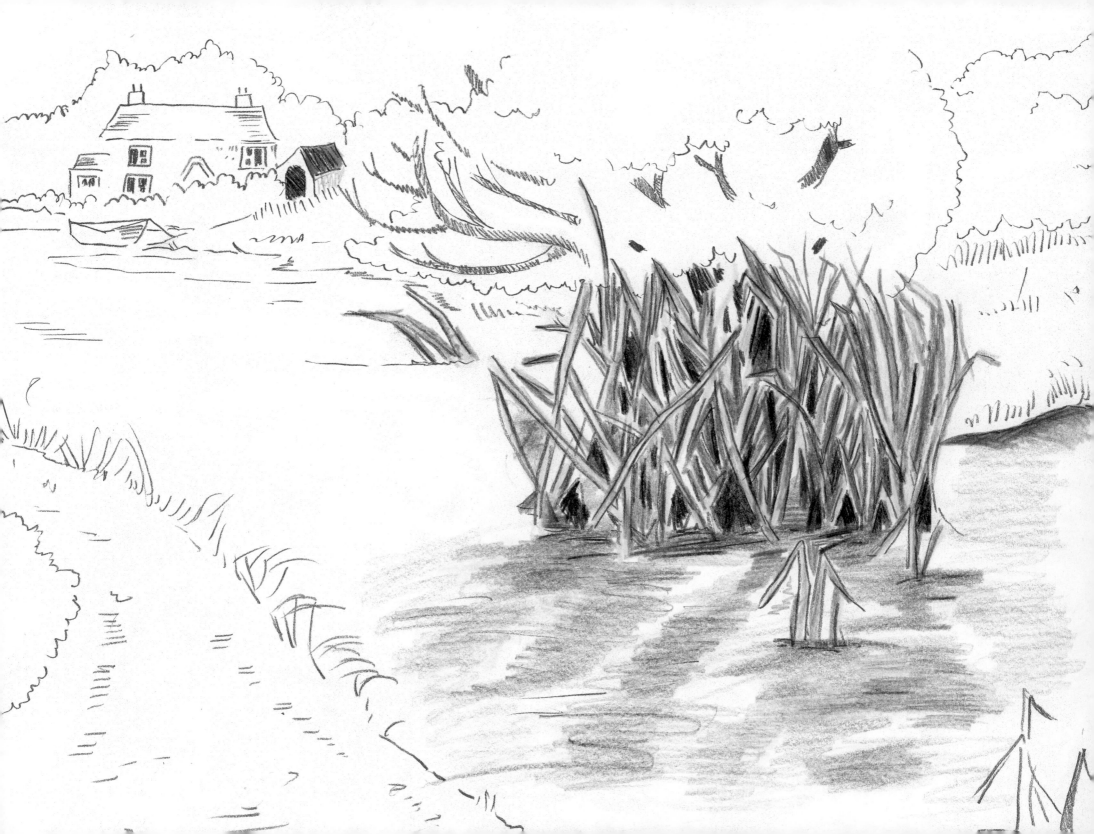

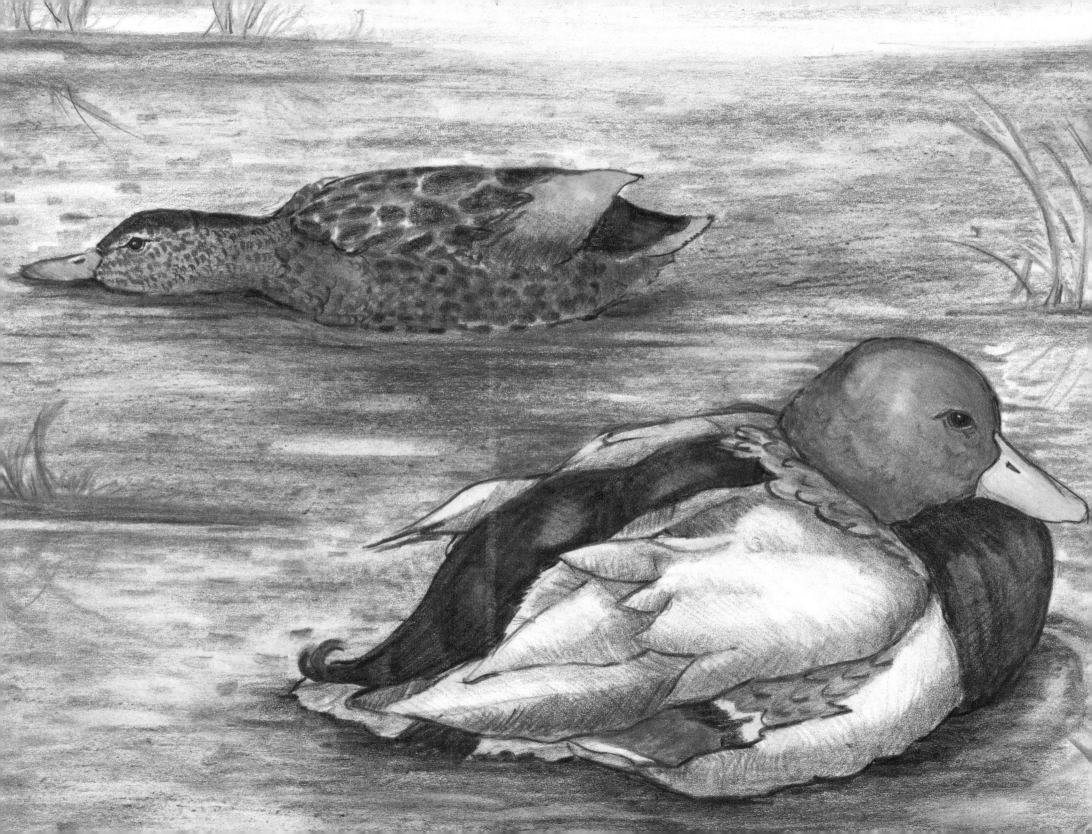

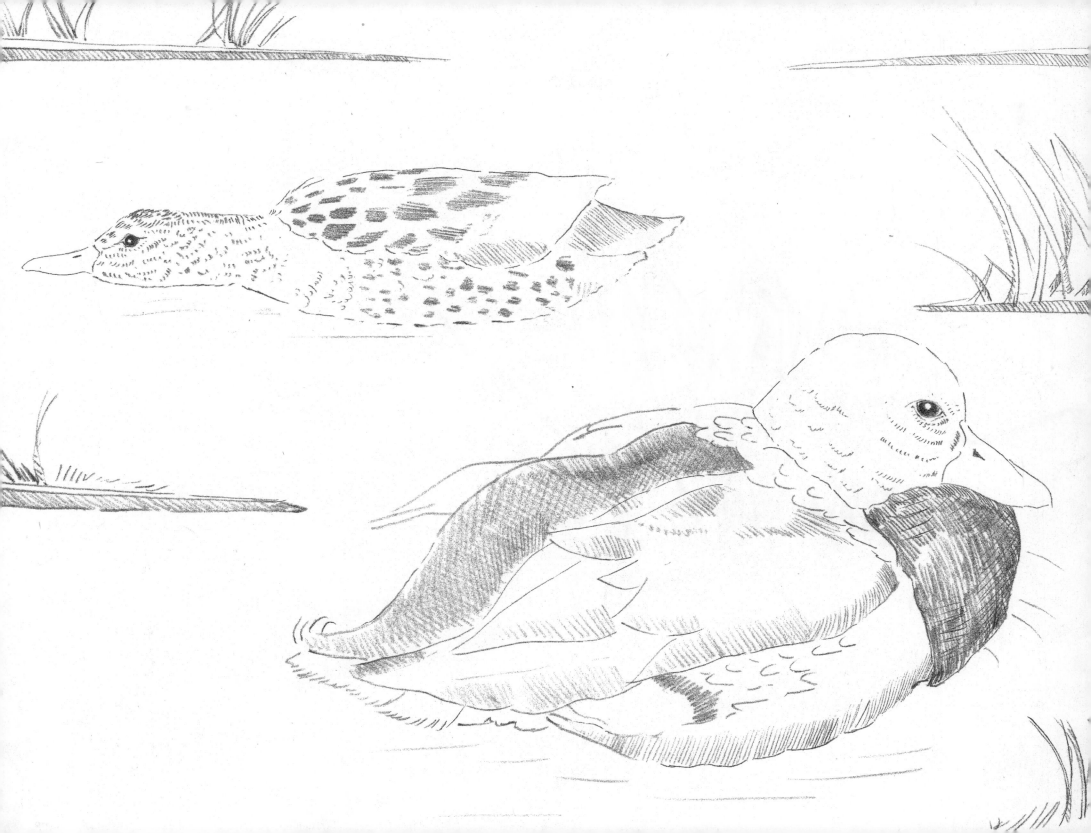

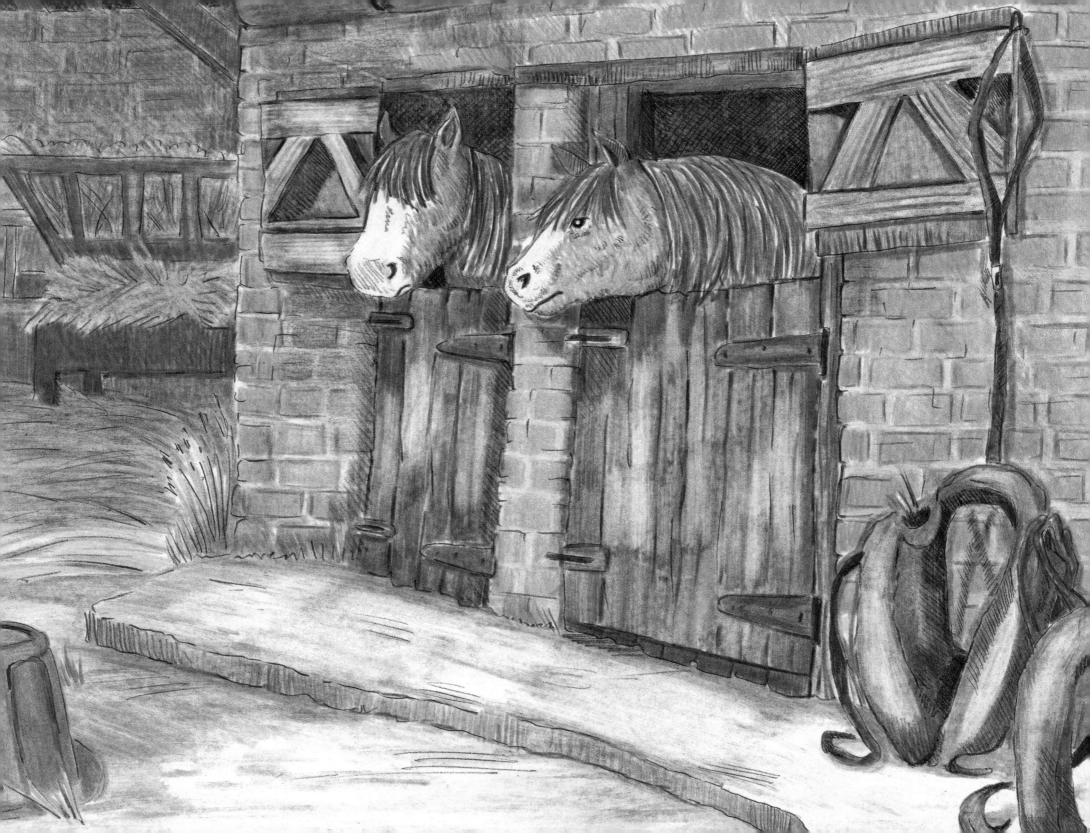

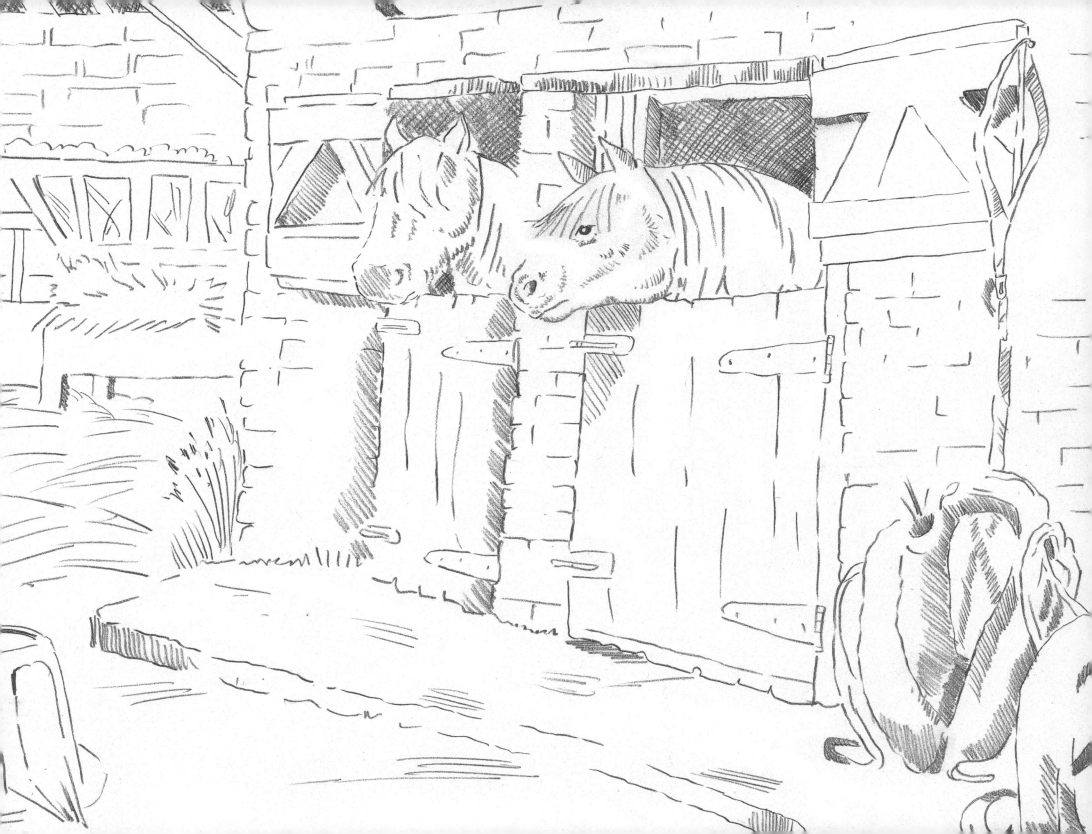

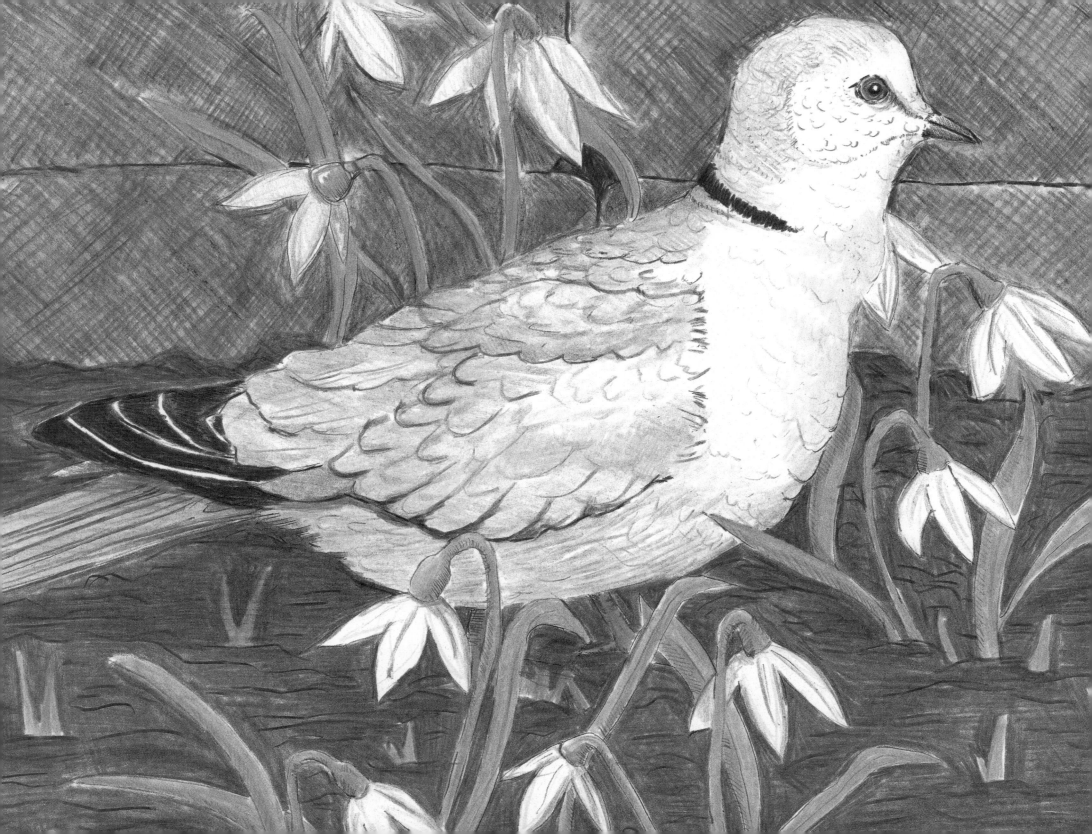

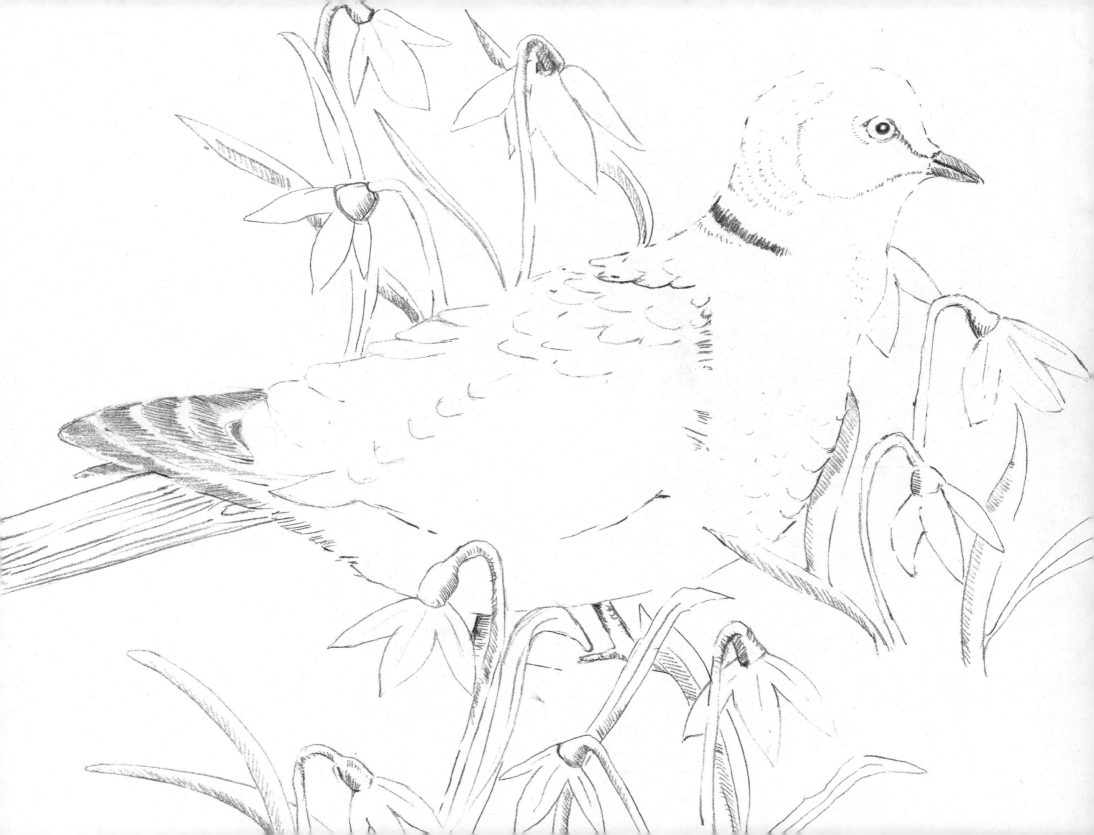

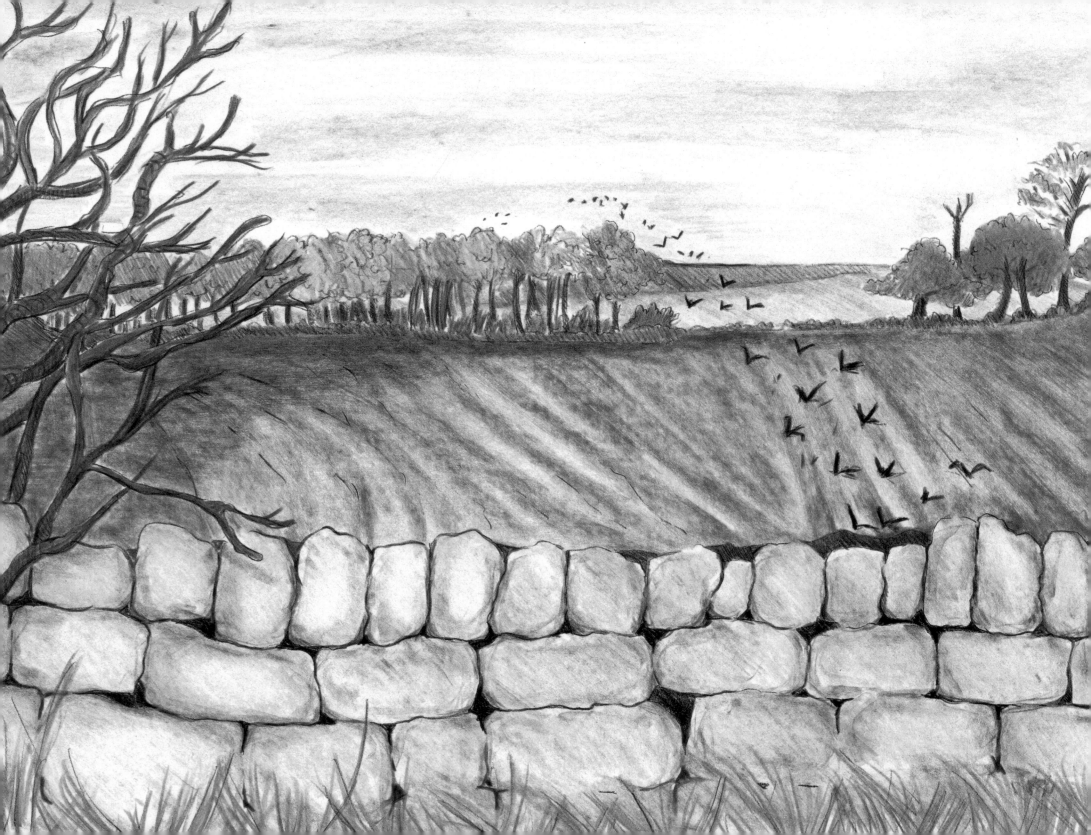

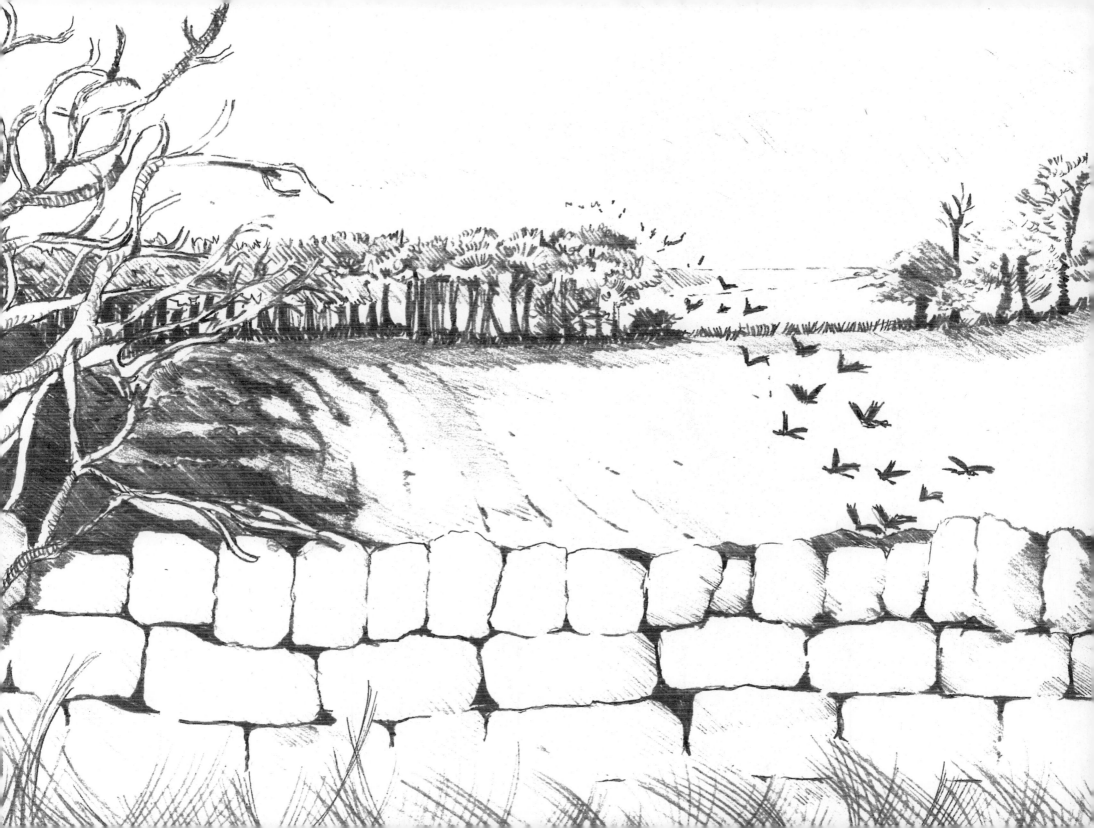

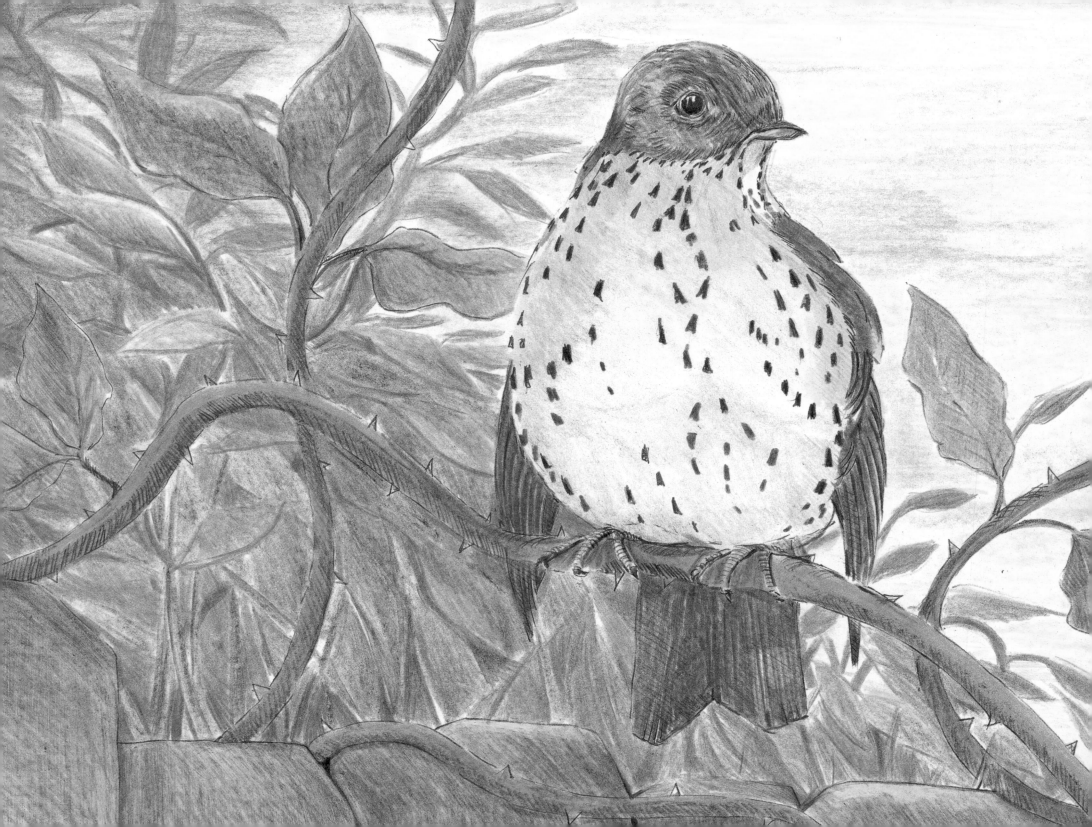

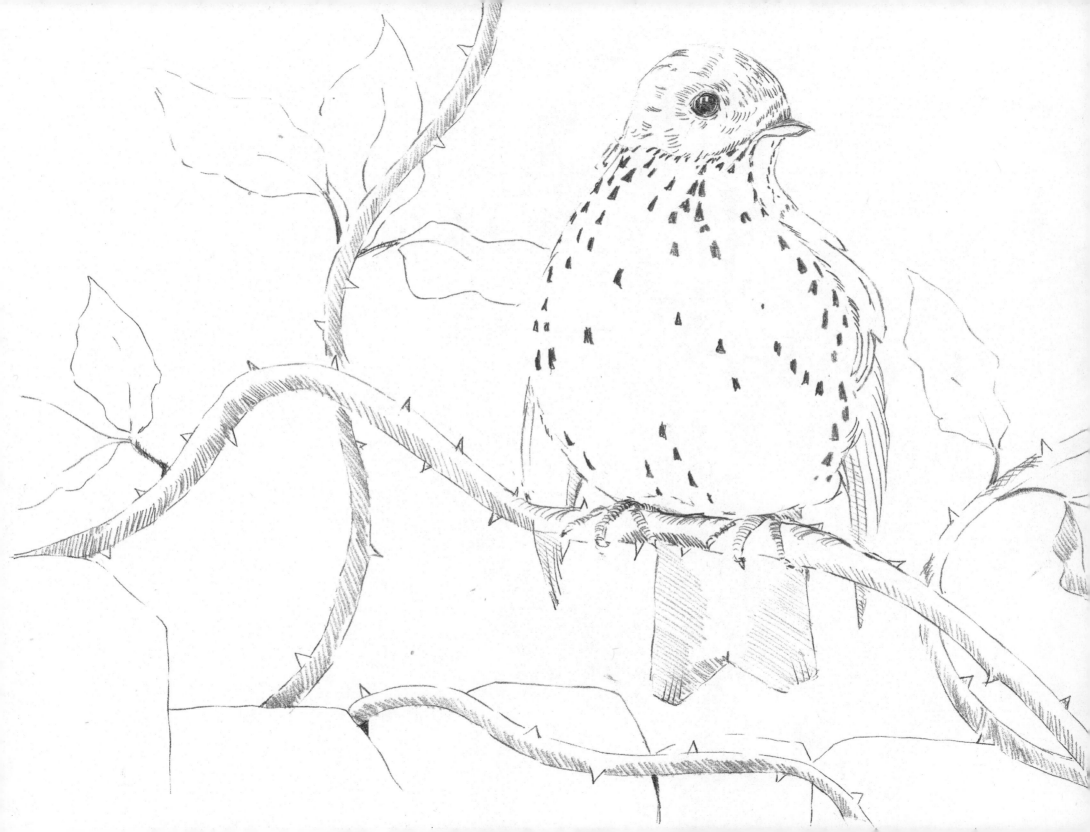

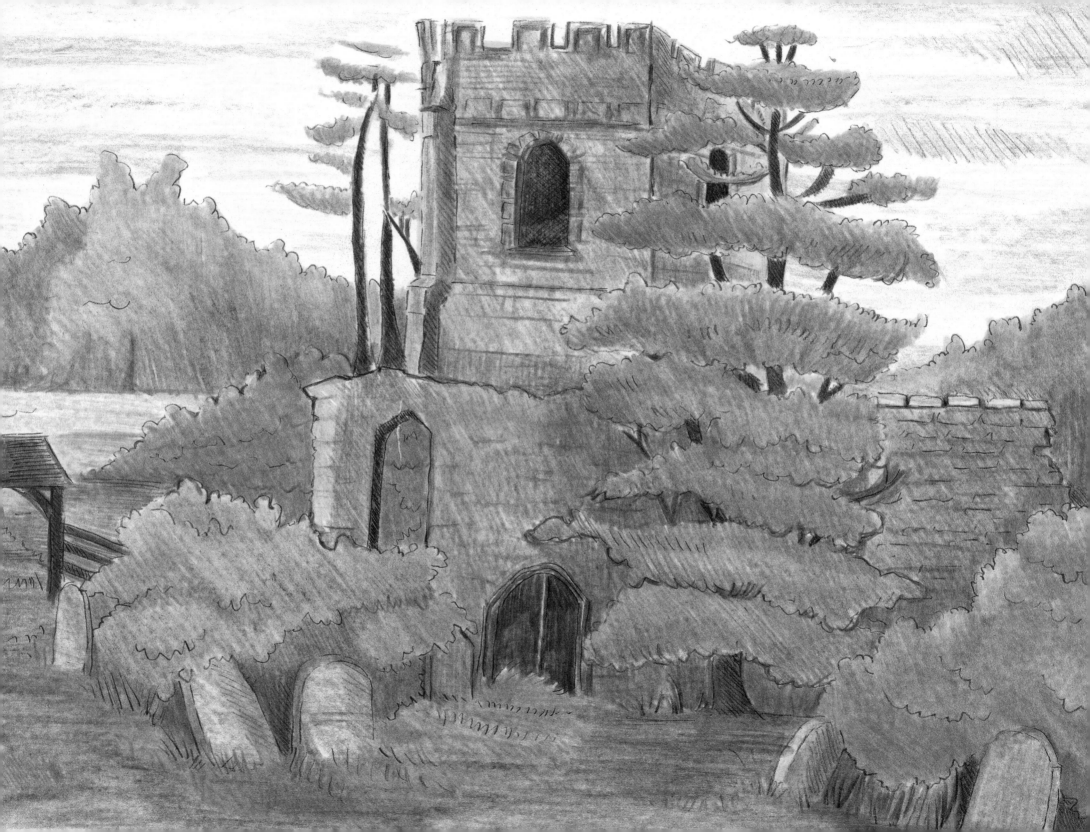

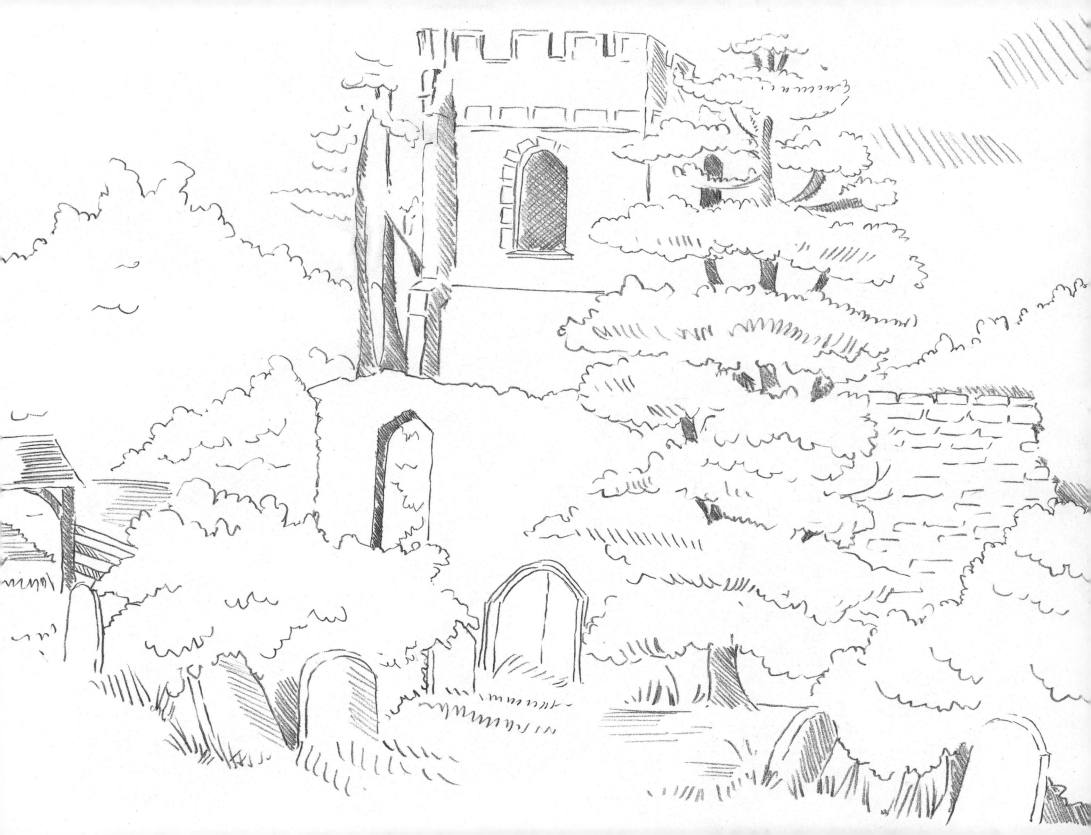

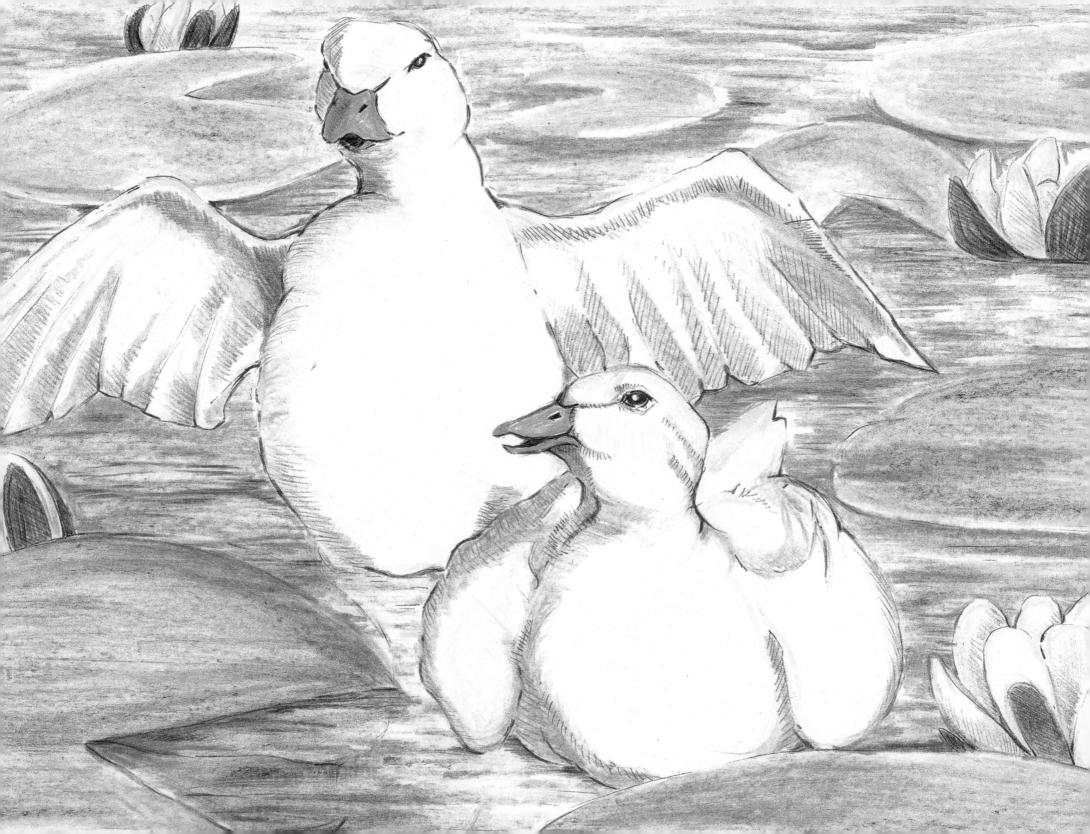

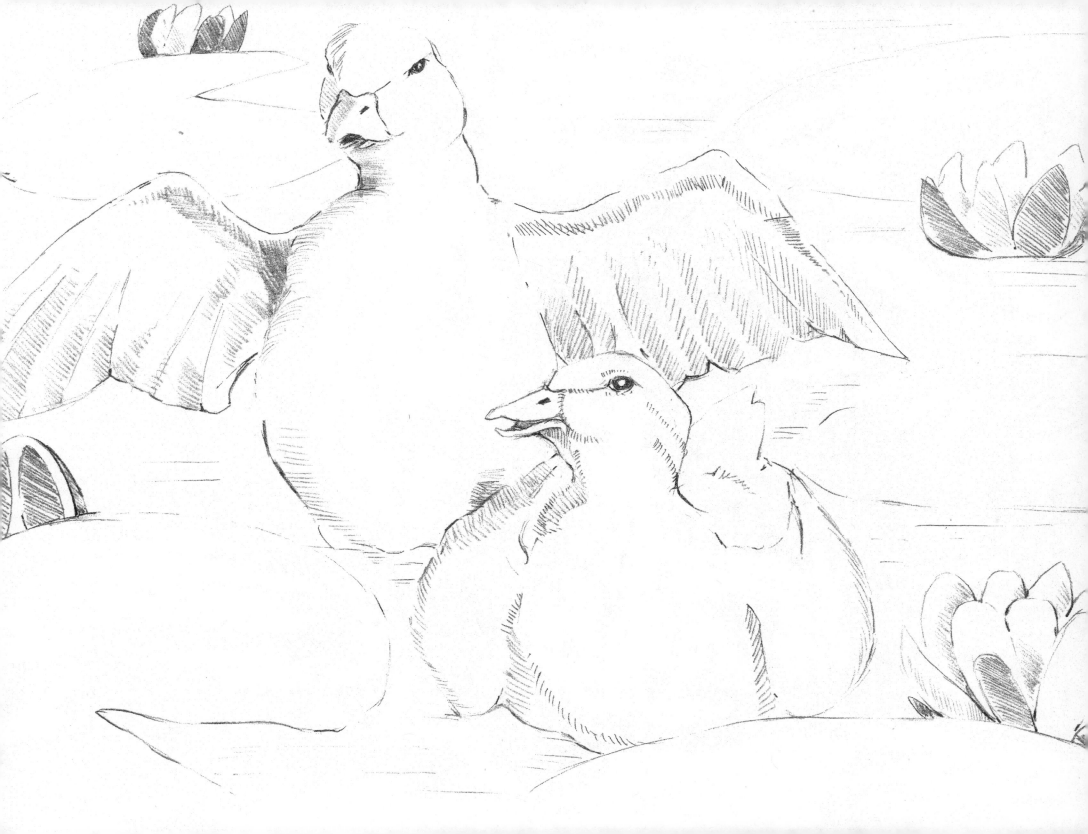

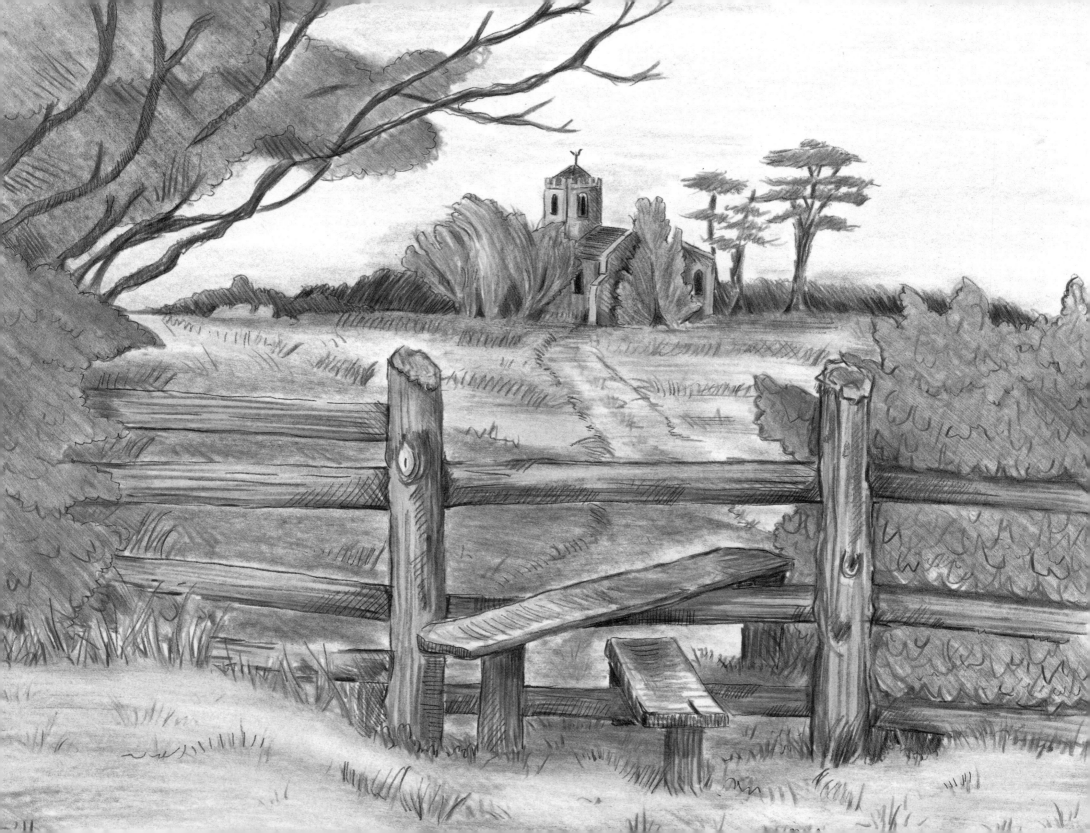

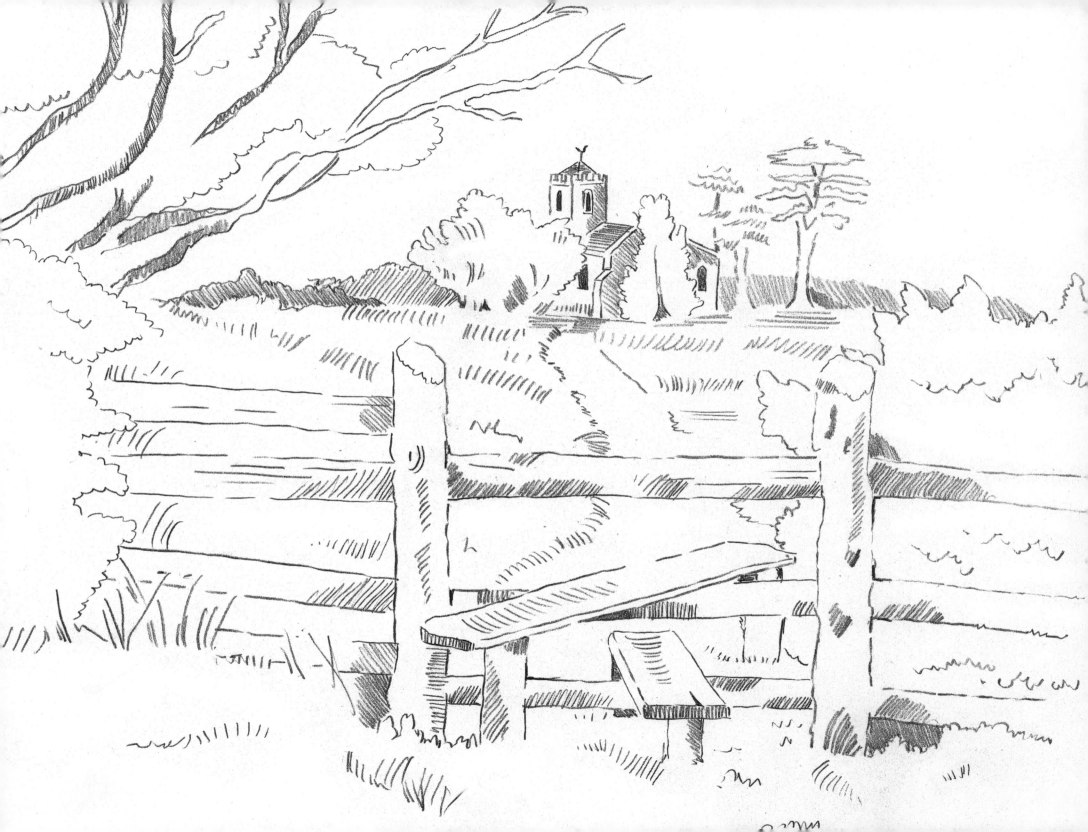

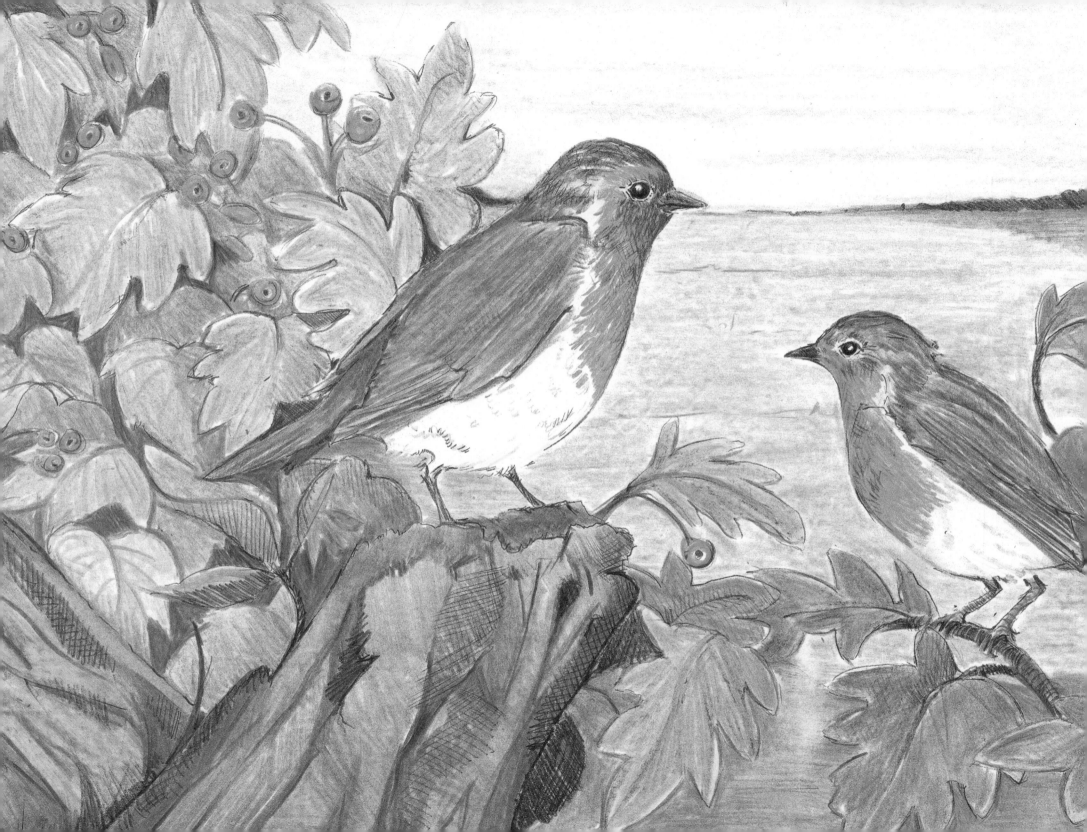

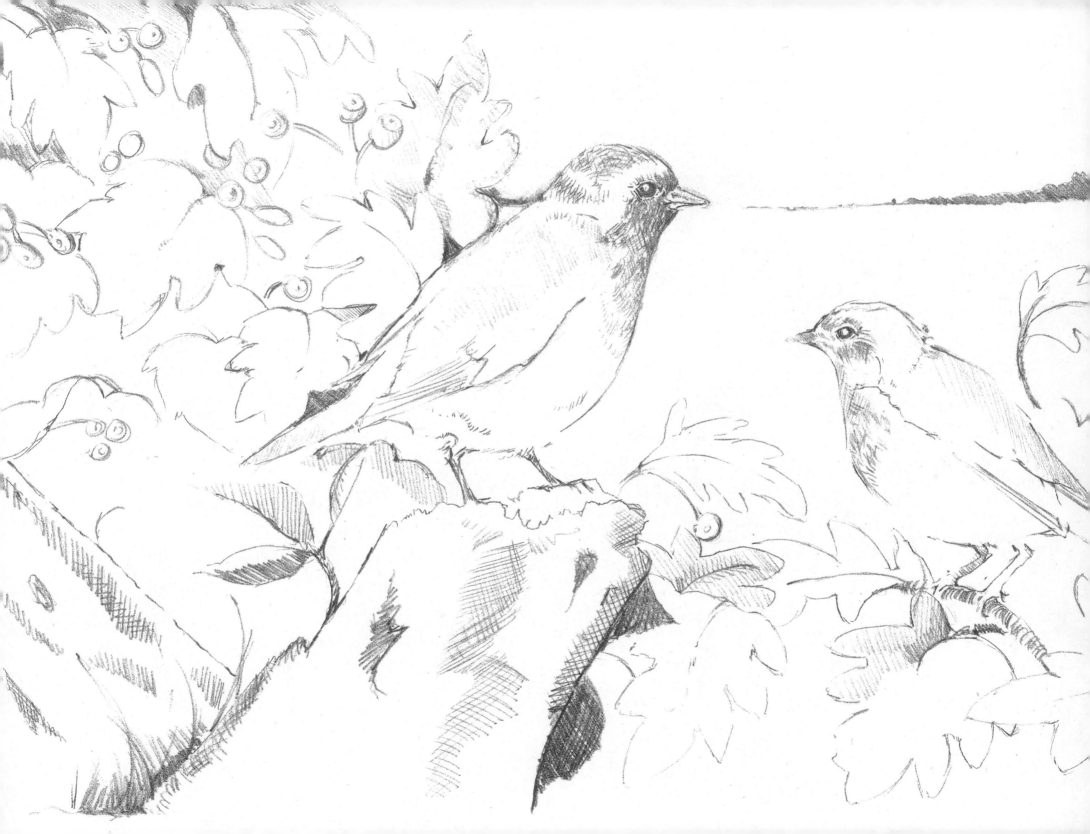

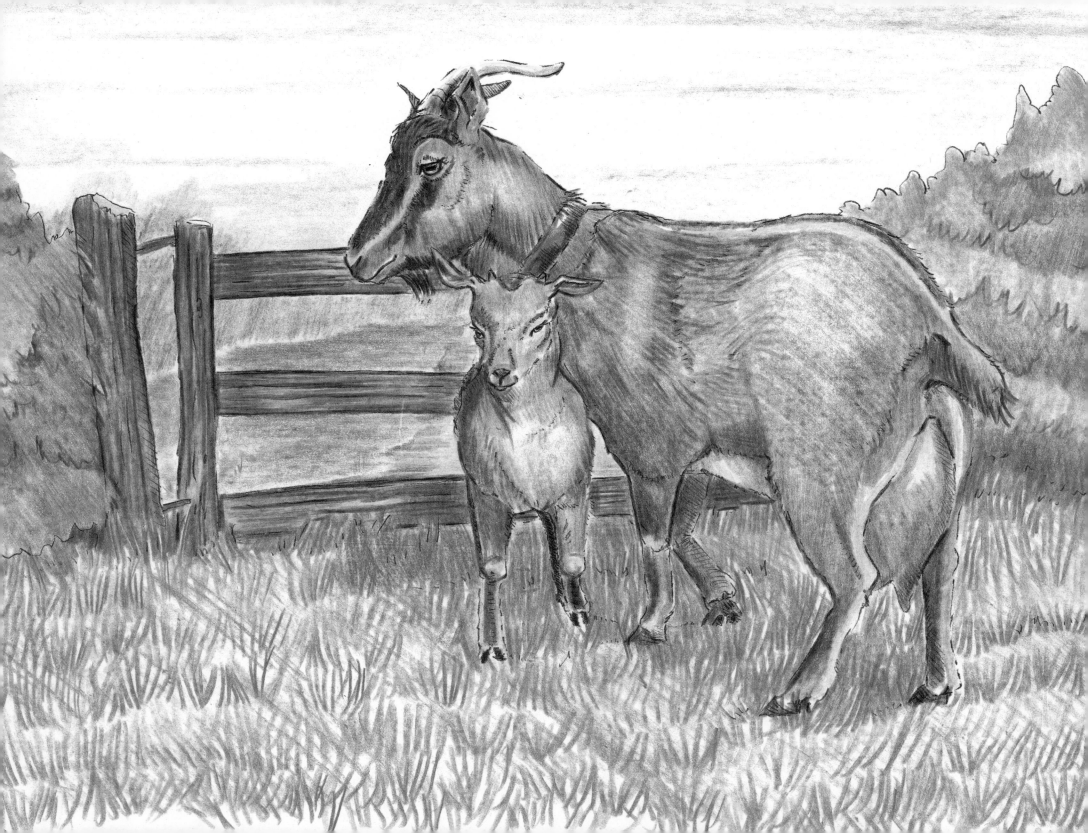

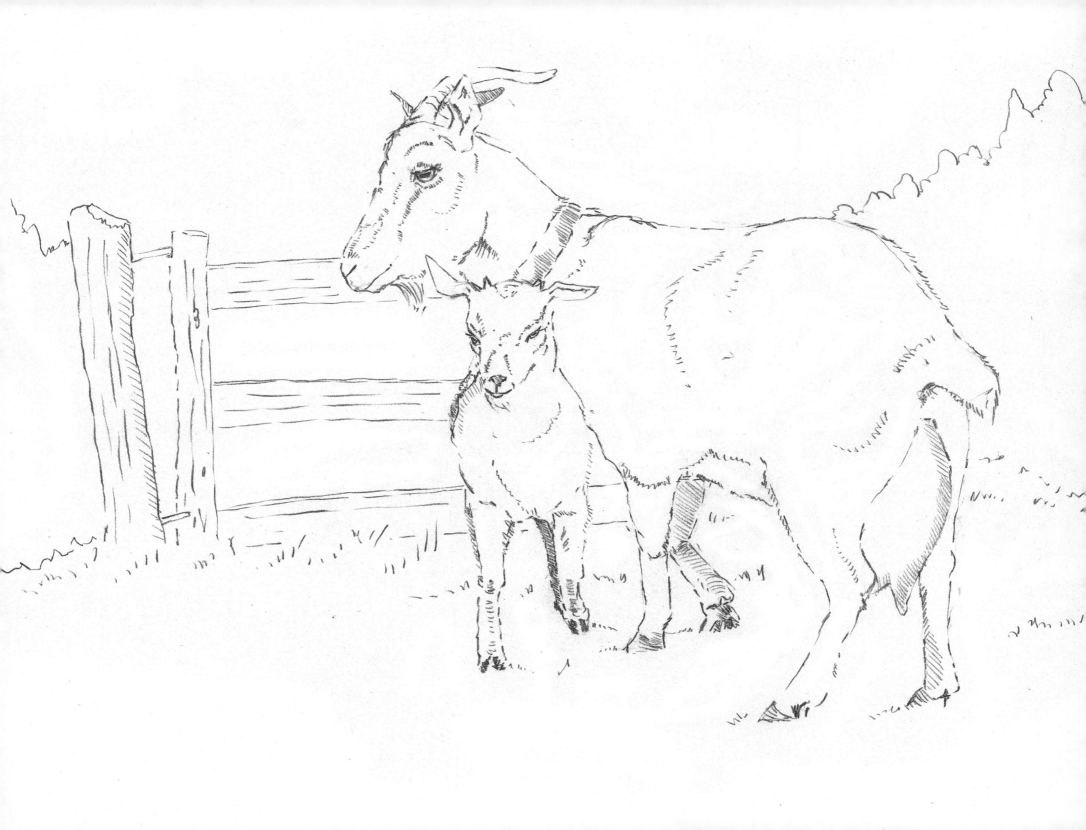

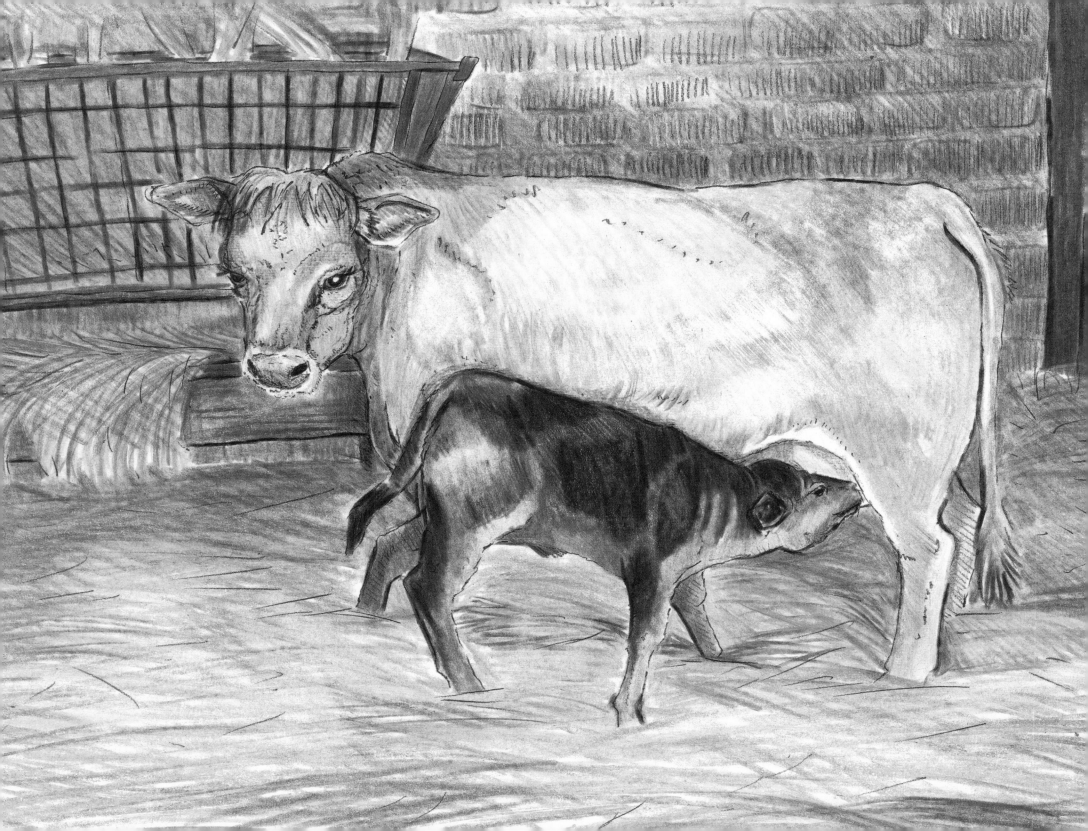

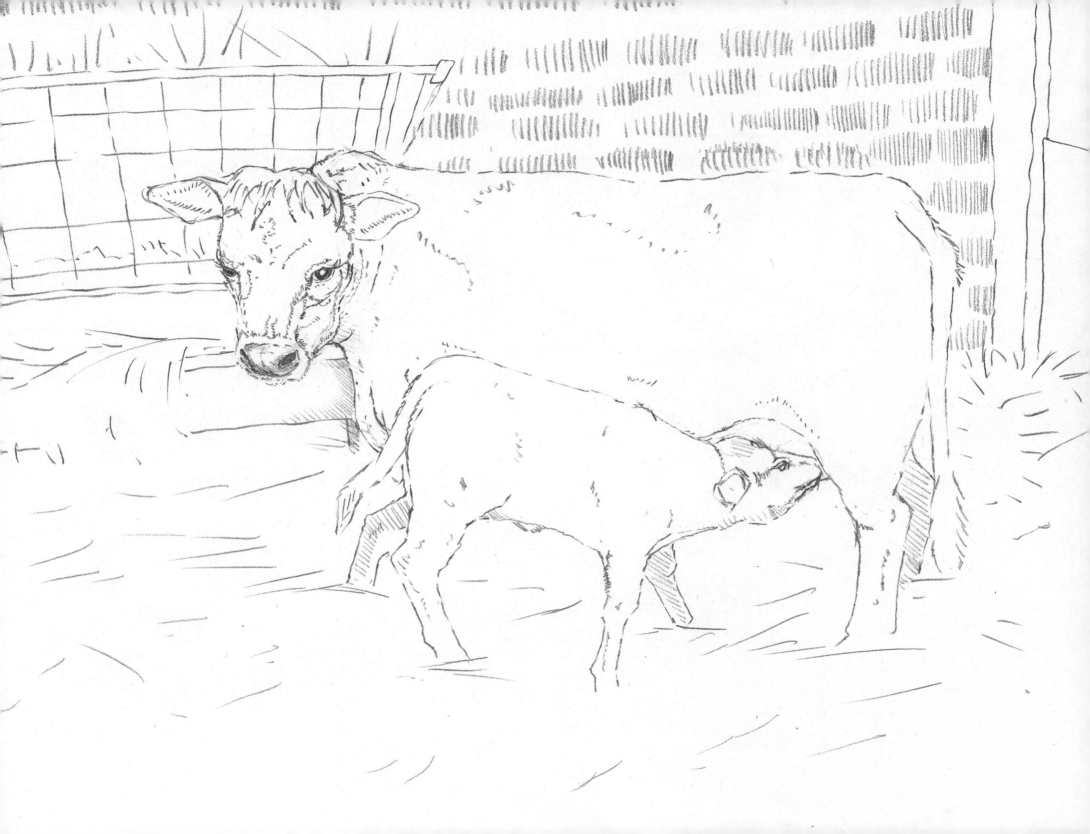

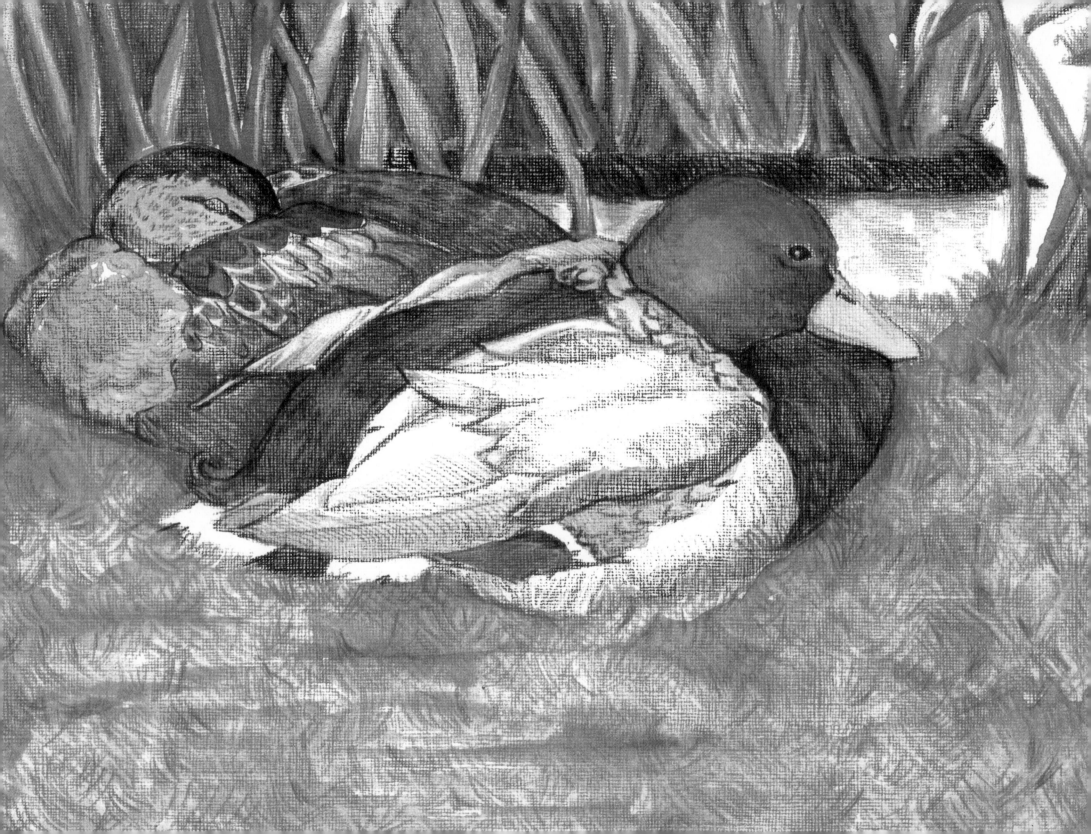

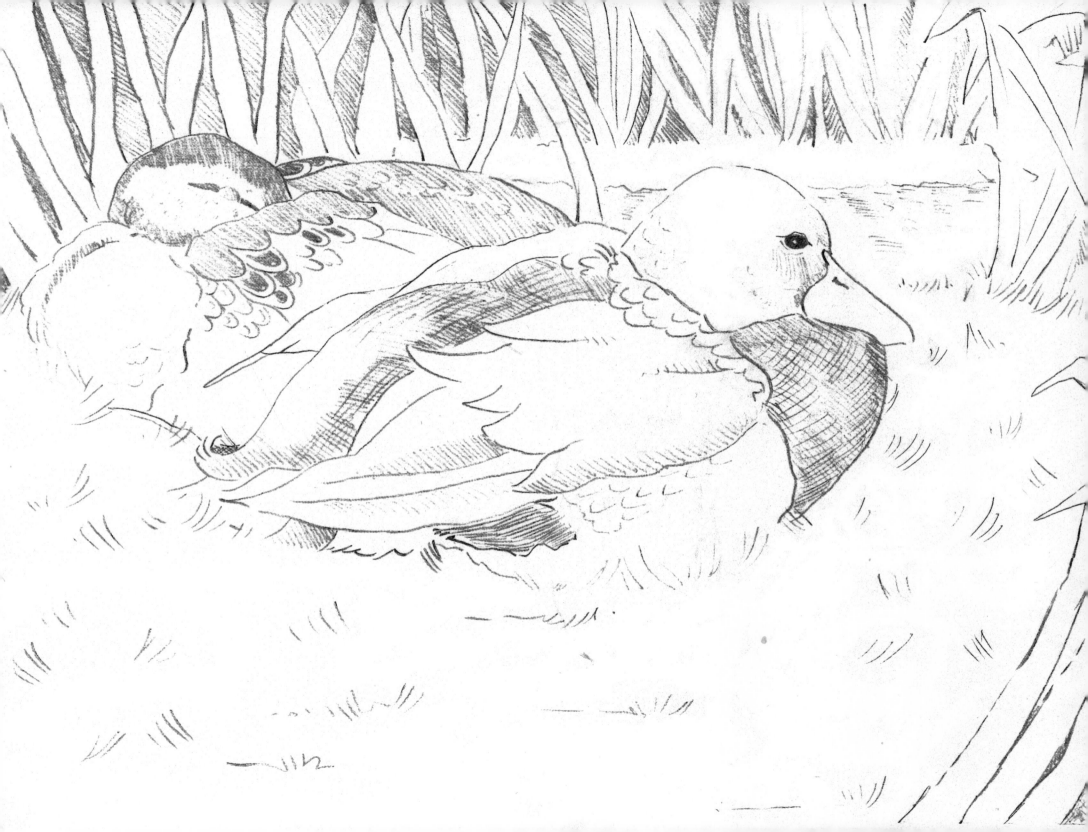

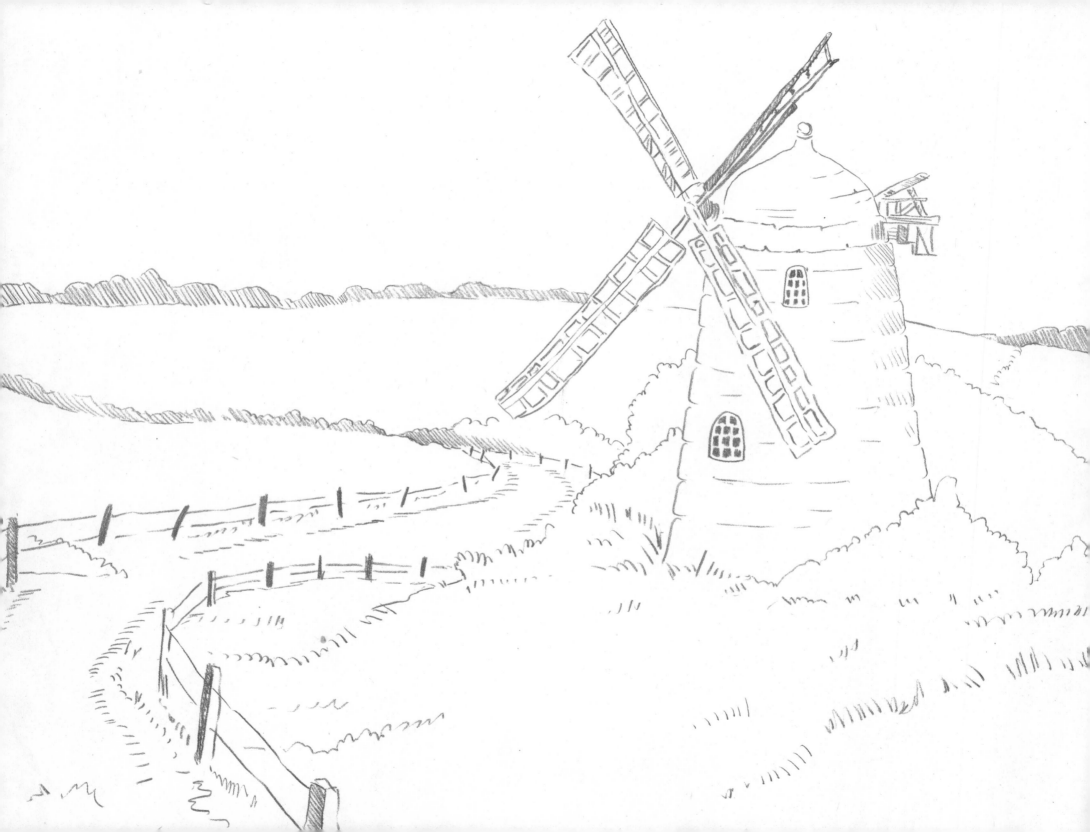